Contents

Published by IPC Magazines Ltd., King's Reach Tower, Stamford Street, London S.E.1., England. Sole Agents for Australia and New Zealand, Gordon & Gotch Ltd.; South Africa, Central News Agency Ltd. Printed in England by Fleetway Printers, Gravesend, Kent. Covers laminated by Olro Coatings using Bexphane film
© Martspress Ltd., 1977.

To Paul
with love
HAPPY XMAS
mummy & Daddy
x x x x x

1. Early one morning, the postman came striding up Toby's garden path. "Ooh! I wonder if he has any mail for me," thought Toby, excitedly. (Do *you* think that when you see the postman coming towards your house? I know that *I* do!)

2. Anyway, this turned out to be one of Toby's lucky days. The postman *did* have something for him. It was an invitation to a fancy dress party in the Town Hall! Toby jumped for joy!

3. Well, on the day of the party, Toby's mother helped him to dress up as a pirate. Toby was thrilled with the costume.

4. *Nothing* could spoil Toby's happiness that day; not even when he passed Bertie Bulldog on his way to the party and Bertie, in his usual sneering way said: "Huh! You won't win any prizes with *that* costume!"

5. As Toby went merrily on his way, however, he was being watched. Lurking among the bushes at the roadside was a bunch of real *live* pirates . . . and what a rough, tough, cut-throat crew they were ! Just *look* at them !

6. The first Toby knew of them was when they grabbed hold of him ! "Why, shiver me timbers !" laughed their captain. "This bold boy will make a fine cabin boy for me ! All nicely dressed up for the part, he is !"

7. Poor Toby ! One moment he was heading towards the fancy dress party in the Town Hall, and the next he was kidnapped by pirates.

8. He was quite, quite helpless as his captors carried him down to the harbour, took him aboard a rowing boat and then set off for their ship, which was bobbing at anchor out in the bay. What *would* become of Toby ?

9. The pirates were very excited. They had stolen a treasure map from another pirate crew and were planning to dig up the treasure and keep it.

10. So that very night they set sail. And what of Toby? Well, he was put to work dusting the furniture in the pirate captain's cabin, and as he did so, what should he come across but the stolen treasure map? A crafty little smile suddenly flitted across Toby's face.

11. He'd had a *splendid* idea. Picking up a pen that lay on the captain's desk, he began to make changes to the map....

12. The voyage to the island was long and tiring—especially for Toby, who was forced to work hard all the time. But at last the island came into sight. What excitement there was on board the ship.

13. The pirates could hardly wait to get ashore. They lowered the ship's sails and dropped anchor near the palm-fringed beach. Then, taking Toby with them, they went ashore in rowing boats. The captain unrolled the map and began to follow the instructions on it.

14. "Now let me see," he said. "We start at this strangely-shaped tree and take fifty paces towards the north. Come on then, lads. Follow me!" he called.

15. Toby stood quietly on one side and watched the pirates following their captain as he began to measure out the paces. Of course, as Toby had changed the map, they went the wrong way!

16. Toby waited until they were out of sight, then he raced to where the treasure was *really* hidden, a place marked by an oddly-shaped rock.

17. Down on his knees flopped Toby, and he began to shovel away the sand with his hands. So fast did he work, that he soon uncovered the treasure chest. Oh, how *thrilling!*

18. His heart thumping with excitement, Toby managed to drag the treasure chest across to the spot where the pirates' boats were beached. Then he lifted it into one of the boats, and raised the sail. The boat began to bob away from the shore.

19. How *angry* the pirates were when they found out how they had been tricked. By then, however, the little boat carrying Toby was far out to sea.

20. Before long, Toby was picked up by a ship of the King's navy. The sailors laughed and cheered when he told them how he had fooled the pirates and made off with their treasure.

21. "The treasure really belongs to His Majesty," said the captain. "It was stolen from him many months ago. But you, Toby, may keep a piece of the treasure as a reward for helping to find it. His Majesty would want you to be so rewarded."

22. So the delighted little Toby chose one of the glittering gold cups out of the chest, and before long, he was back home and telling his mother and father all about his exciting adventure.

23. A few days later, Toby met Bertie Bulldog once more. "I bet that costume you wore for the fancy dress party didn't win a prize!" scoffed Bertie.

24. "As a matter of fact, old chap, I 'won' a gold cup!" said Toby, with a grin. Mind you, he didn't explain that the cup was his reward for helping to find the King's treasure!

Patty and her Magic Puppy

DO you have a puppy as a pet? Lots of girls and boys do, you know, and there's nothing very special about that.

Patty's puppy, Poppy, however, was very special indeed. You see, Poppy was a *magic* puppy! Simply by wagging her bushy little tail she could make all *sorts* of wonderful things happen.

Take the day of this story, for instance. It was a lovely, warm, sunny summer's day. Birds were twittering their sweet little songs as they winged their way from tree-top to tree-top, and bees were buzzing busily as they flitted from flower to flower. It was the sort of day when one of the very nicest things anyone could think of doing would be to go for a picnic in the countryside. So that's what Patty did!

Helped by her mummy, the little girl packed a picnic basket with lots of nice things for Poppy and herself to eat. Then, bidding Mummy a cheerful farewell, Patty and her puppy set out along one of the lovely tree-lined lanes that passed by their cottage.

It didn't take them long to find a pretty little picnic-place. Patty spread out her picnic cloth on the ground and laid out all the food, and very soon the pair of them were tucking into their meal.

"Ah, this is the life, Poppy!" said Patty with a contented smile, as she settled herself comfortably on the soft, green grass, and Poppy—who by this time had finished eating and had also stretched out on the grass—yawned sleepily, as if to say: "It certainly is."

The two of them would have been quite happy to have spent the rest of the afternoon just lazing around like that. Alas, however, they didn't get the chance to do so.

Patty suddenly gave a little shiver as a cool breeze blew over her. She looked up and saw that dark clouds were now rolling across the sky and blotting out the sunshine.

A moment or two later . . . SPLASH! A

floated gently into the air like a magical flying carpet, and when Patty and Poppy climbed on to the cloth, it whisked them all the way home without them getting even a teeny *weeny* bit wet.

Gosh! Wouldn't it be *thrilling* to have a puppy like Poppy as a pet?

I mean to say, there are all *sorts* of ways Poppy can help her young mistress.

There was another day, for instance, when Patty and her mummy and Poppy were out for a walk and—just as in this story—it began to rain. So do you know what Poppy did

raindrop landed on Patty's forehead. It was followed by another . . . then another . . . then another.

Yes, sad to say a shower of rain had begun to fall, and Patty could tell from the dark grey colour of the clouds that the rain was going to get very much heavier before very long.

"Oh, dear, Poppy—we're going to get *awfully* wet!" she said, anxiously packing their belongings into the picnic basket.

Patty had forgotten all about Poppy's magic, however, and at times like this the wonderful little puppy seemed to know *just* what to do.

She padded on to the picnic cloth and wagged her tail, and do you know what happened? — POP! — the picnic cloth

then? No, I won't spoil it for you by telling you here! You can read all about it by turning to the "Patty and her Magic Puppy" story on Page 56!

* * * *

Pixie Fun
with
little Pixie Bumpkin

1. Dear old Granny Smith was busy picking apples in the orchard. Pixie Bumpkin often helped Granny Smith with the work on her farm, so she said he could have an apple any time he wanted. Pixie took one gladly.

2. Pixie went to see Mr. Candy next. Mr. Candy worked in the sweet shop, and he was stirring a great big pot full of toffee when Pixie came in. "Hello, Pixie," he said. "I'm making sweets to sell at the market."

3. Now Pixie loved watching Mr. Candy at work and he skipped over to take a closer look at what his friend the sweet-maker was doing. "Take care," said Mr. Candy—but he was too late. Pixie dropped his apple into the toffee!

4. Mr. Candy snatched a fork out of a drawer and used it to lift the apple out of the toffee. "Oh, I *am* sorry!" gasped Pixie. Mr. Candy smiled at him. "Never mind," said he. "This has given me an idea!"

5. "Instead of making sweets to sell at the market, I'll make *toffee apples!*" he chuckled. "The only problem is, where can I get some apples?" Pixie's eyes lit up. "You can leave that to me, Mr. Candy," he said. Then he ran back to Granny Smith.

6. And when Granny heard about Mr. Candy's idea of making lots of toffee apples to sell at the market. she was only too pleased to give Pixie all the apples he could carry. How happy the other pixies were to buy the *yummy* toffee apples.

There are six sweets hidden in this picture. Can you find them all?

Fun at school with Miss Muddle

1. The pupils in Miss Muddle's class at Jolly Towers School are very fond of their teacher. She is always so kind to them. At Christmas, for instance, she baked a Christmas cake especially for those lucky children.

2. She got in an *awful* muddle. Still, she did her best, and that's what matters most. Anyway, before going to school, she filled a spare cake box with breadcrumbs and crusts to feed the ducks on the village pond.

3. It was when Miss Muddle began to toss tit-bits to the ducks, however, that her plans went wrong. You see, that muddle-headed lady fed those lucky ducks with her *Christmas cake* instead of the crumbs and crusts she had put into the other box!

4. She went happily on her way, still not realising that she had made such a silly mistake! Oh, dear! What a big disappointment she was going to have when she found out!

5. "As this is our last day at school before the Christmas holidays, girls and boys," she told her class, "I have a special treat for you." But how the teacher's face fell when she saw the breadcrumbs and crusts.

6. Poor Miss Muddle felt ever so sad at having spoiled the children's surprise present. Still, she cheered up when the children told her they had saved up their pocket money and bought a present for *her.*

7. And you'll never *guess* what the pupils had bought for their teacher. It was a really lovely Christmas cake! "Why, it's *much* nicer than the one I baked! *Thank* you, my dears!" said the teacher joyfully.

8. She shared the cake with her merry little pupils of course, and that was the start of a very happy Christmas for Miss Muddle and her class. And they hope Christmas will be just as happy a time for you, too, girls and boys.

THE SINGING DRAGON

Down the winding path which led from a snug stone cottage towards a lake, ran two children. They were on holiday with their Mummy and Daddy in Scotland, and they were going to stay for a fortnight.

The little boy was called Tom, and every day he went fishing in the lake with his sister Alison, who was a year or so older than he was.

This particular morning, Tom and Alison could hardly see the lake as they drew near to its shore. It was a misty sort of morning, everywhere quiet and still.

Alison was glad she had put on a warm jumper. "This fog is a bit shivery," she said.

Tom lowered his line into the water. "It's only mist, not fog, and the sun will soon warm it away," he said.

"Well, I hope it does," said Alison. "It seems to be the kind of morning for monsters, and I don't want to meet one."

Tom stared at her. "Monsters?" he said. "There are no such things as monsters!"

Suddenly a deep voice floated across the lake towards them. "There are lots of dragons though," it said.

Tom and Alison jumped back several feet.

"Wh—what was that?" stuttered Tom.

"It's me, young fellow, can't you see me?" said the deep voice.

As the early morning mist began to disappear and the sun shone through, Tom and Alison saw the most peculiar creature.

It was—it was—They looked at each other in dismay. Was it a dragon? They just couldn't tell for sure.

"I hope you are not frightened of me, children," went on the curious-looking animal. "I'm very friendly and kind."

Tom cleared his throat and managed to say: "What are you?"

"I'm a dragon, of course," replied the creature.

"Dragons aren't usually friendly. They're not often green, either," Alison said doubtfully. "I've read lots of stories about dragons, and they don't live in lakes usually."

"Well, I agree I'm rather a strange dragon," said the dragon. "I enjoy living in the lake. I like being green, too. Most of all, I like being friendly. But I *am* a real dragon, and what's more, I can sing!"

"Sing? Can you sing songs?" asked Tom.

The dragon nodded. "Yes, indeed," it said. And it stood up in the water and began to sing in a deep, deep voice.

Now the children's daddy was very fond of music, and the kind of music he liked best was opera music. So when the green dragon started to sing, the children knew straight away *what* he was singing, because they had heard that song many times before.

"It's just like Daddy's records," said Tom.

The dragon finished his song and smiled happily at the children.

"What do you think?" he asked. "Not a bad voice, eh?"

"*Lovely*," said Alison.

Tom had an idea.

"Would you like to come and sing for my Daddy?" he asked. "He has missed being able to play his records. It would be a wonderful surprise for him."

The dragon looked doubtful. "I don't really like to leave the lake," he said.

Tom and Alison thought quickly. "How about the bath?" Alison whispered in Tom's ear.

"He'd never get in it," Tom replied.

"Yes, he would," said Alison. "With a bit of a squeeze he could. And daddy would love the music!"

They turned back to the dragon. "Could you manage in the bath?" asked Alison. "It's a very big old-fashioned bath. Please?"

The dragon chuckled. "Oh, very well," he said. "It's worth a try. I don't often have an audience!"

"We'll go and fill the bath," said Tom breathlessly.

They ran back up the path and into the cottage. Alison put the plug in the big old bath and turned on the taps.

The bath was only half full when they heard a heavy sploshing noise and turned to see the dragon's head framed in the bathroom door. He looked rather worried but he brightened when he saw the bath. With a tremendous slither and a wriggle and a splash, he was in it.

Water sploshed over the edge of the bath and Alison quickly turned off the taps.

"Very comfortable," grinned the dragon, settling back. "Exactly the right temperature, too. Shall I begin?"

"Yes, please," cried Tom, jumping up and down with excitement.

The dragon opened his mouth, took a deep breath, and began to sing.

Tom and Alison sat down side by side on the floor, closed their eyes and listened. . . .

*   *   *   *

Suddenly Alison felt a touch on her shoulder, and a laughing voice cried: "Hey, you two! Wake up! See what Daddy has bought."

Alison opened her eyes. The music was still there, lovely golden music . . . but she wasn't in the bathroom. She was back at the lakeside. Tom was beside her, just waking up. Mummy was there, and Daddy was holding a tiny transistor radio from which music was pouring.

"What do you think of Daddy's new radio?" Mummy asked. "We saw it in the village and decided to buy it."

"But we found a dragon to sing for—" began Tom sleepily, but Alison nudged him and he stopped.

"A dragon?" said Mummy. "What are you talking about?"

"It's just a story we were reading," said Alison quickly.

"Come on then, children," said Mummy. "It's time for lunch."

The two children stopped outside the cottage door.

"Did you dream about a singing dragon?" asked Tom.

"Yes, I did," whispered Alison. "Was it really a dream? He seemed so real!"

An angry shout from the bathroom interrupted her.

"Whatever have you two been doing in the bathroom?" asked Daddy crossly. "There's water all over the floor!"

Tom looked at Alison, and Alison looked at Tom. But they never did decide for certain whether they had talked to a singing, green, friendly dragon, or not. . . .

Grandma- next door

1. Pam and Paul are lucky enough to live right next door to their Grandma, and they were playing in her garden one Spring day when Daddy spoke to them over the fence. "I have a *surprise* for you two," he smiled.

2. Now Pam and Paul just *love* surprises, so they waved goodbye to Grandma and scampered back to their own garden. And oh, how excited they were when they saw the surprise. It was a nesting box for birds!

3. Daddy fixed up the nesting box among the branches of a tree, and before many days had gone by, a pair of beautiful little bluetits decided it would make a very nice home for them. Pam and Paul were thrilled.

4. When the birds had built their nest in the box, Mrs. Bluetit settled down to lay her eggs and then hatch them. While she was busy doing so, Mr. Bluetit flew to and from the nesting box, bringing food for his wife.

5. The eggs were hatched within around two weeks of being laid, and when another three weeks or so had gone by, the baby birds were preparing to fly away. All this time, the children had watched them.

6. Pam and Paul had *so* enjoyed watching the baby birds that they were really quite sad when the birds all flew away. Still, it so happened that Grandma heard Pam tell Paul what a pity it was that the birds had gone.

7. Well, you know what a dear old soul Grandma is. She wondered how she could cheer the children up . . . and she soon thought of a way. She bought a surprise gift for Pam and Paul.

8. Look! Grandma's present was a *cuckoo clock,* with a bird that popped in and out of its little wooden house all day long just as the bluetits had done! And *this* bird wouldn't fly away! How *kind* Grandma was!

Names from here and there

Have you ever wondered how a town came to be called, for instance, Kingston? Or why Grimsby is called Grimsby, or how Dundee got its name? There is a good reason. You see, in the days of the Anglo-Saxons the word TON meant farm. So Kingston means king's farm, Aston means eastern farm, Ryton means river farm, and so on.

DUN meant fort in the old Gaelic language of Scotland. So Dundee, Dunbar and Dunoon would all have had forts long ago, probably on a hill top.

CASTRUM is a Roman word for camp or fort. So when the Romans invaded this country, they named many towns like Doncaster, Lancaster and Chester.

ABER meant the mouth of a river, or the joining of two rivers. So it is easy to see how Aberdeen, Aberdare and Aberystwyth were given their names.

BY meant a village. Thus Kirkby or Kirby meant church village, Whitby meant white village and Grimsby is named after a man—Grim's village.

EY is another Anglo-Saxon word, meaning island. Have you heard of Athelney? It means "island of the princes". Ramsey means "wild garlic island", and you must have heard of Sheppey and Thorney.

POOL, of course, meant a small lake. And so Blackpool was named because it grew up beside a lake of dark water. Then there are also Poole, Welshpool, Liverpool and Hartlepool.

PRETTY KITTY

KITTY'S missing!
Oh, dear me!
Where, oh where
Can Kitty be?

We've hunted here,
We've hunted there;
We've hunted for her
Everywhere!

But hark! I hear
A tiny purr.
I've caught a glimpse
Of ginger fur.

Yes, *there* she is!
Well, fancy that!
She's been asleep
In Grandma's hat!

Teddy's Toyland Alphabet

A **a**

A is for Animals.
Two by two
They march around
The Toyland zoo.

B is for Bubbles,
Floating by,
Then drifting upwards
To the sky.

B **b**

C **c**

C is for Cradle.
Ssh! Let's peep!
Ooh, look! The babe
Is fast asleep.

D
d

D is for Dolly,
*   Who's hoping to wear*
A chain of daisies
*   In her hair.*

E is for Elf,
*   Who's full of fun.*
He has a smile
*   For everyone.*

E
e

F
f

F is for Flag
*   To wave on high,*
Whene'er the Toyland
*   Queen goes by.*

G

g

G is for Games.
It's wet today,
And so indoors
I'll have to play.

H is for Harness,
A pretty blue,
So Dobbin can give
A ride to you.

H

h

I

i

I is for Islands,
One—two—three,
Far, far across
The Toyland sea.

J

j

J is for Jack
   Inside a box.
He springs right out
   When someone knocks.

K is for Kite.
   Upon the breeze
It soars above
   The tallest trees.

K

k

L

l

L is for Lorry.
   With its load,
It bowls along
   A Toyland road.

M

m

M is for Music.
　The Toyland band
Is loved by all
　Throughout the land.

N is for Net.
　Oh, how I wish
That I could catch
　Some little fish.

N

n

O

o

O is for Oars,
　For rowing a boat.
What fun it is
　To be afloat.

P **p**

P is for Pilot,
Up in the air.
He's circling above
The Toyland fair.

Q is for Quaint—
The way Teddy looks,
Dressed like the King
In the story-books.

Q **q**

R **r**

R is for Rocking-horse.
Up I go,
Then merrily
Rock to and fro.

S **s**

S is for Skates.
    It's oh, so nice
When you can glide
    Across the ice.

T is for Toboggan.
    What a thrill,
To whizz right down
    A snowy hill.

T **t**

U **u**

U is for Umbrella
    To keep us dry.
When rain is falling,
    We hold it high.

V

v

V is for Voyage,
O'er the sea.
Now don't you wish
That you were me?

W is for Wind,
And when it blows
The windmill's sail
A-whirring goes.

W

W

X

x

X is for Xylophone,
Fun to play.
I learn a new tune
Every day.

Y

Y

Y is for Yule-tide,
   Full of cheer;
A lovely way
   To end each year.

Z is for Zebra,
   Which, of course,
Looks rather like
   A stripey horse!

Z

z

Sing a Song of Sixpence

Sing a song of sixpence,
  A pocket full of rye;
Four and twenty blackbirds
  Baked in a pie.
When the pie was opened,
  The birds began to sing;
Wasn't that a dainty dish
  To set before the king?

POPPYSEED THE ELF

1. Poppyseed the elf was always getting into mischief. If he wasn't up to one trick he was up to another. So when he decided to visit his friend the witch, Rosepetal the fairy, was worried.

2. "Please don't go," she said, "you always get into trouble when you go to the witch's house." But Poppyseed marched straight into the witch's house and sat down. "I would like to be a mouse," he said.

3. The witch was very surprised, but she was used to Poppyseed's strange ideas. She found her book of spells, waved her magic wand and spoke the magic words. Before you could say "Abracadabra" there was a mouse sitting on the chair instead of an elf. "Thank you!" squeaked Poppyseed-the-mouse, and away he scampered.

4. He had lots of exciting adventures in the woods. He met squirrels and rabbits and many other little creatures. But when the night-time came, and all his new friends went home to bed, Poppyseed was frightened. He quickly found a hole to hide in, where he would be safe from a big white owl which came swooping down.

5. When he woke up, the sun was shining again. "Now for some more adventures," thought Poppyseed, running out of his hole. He didn't see the big black cat which was lying in wait to catch him.

6. "Help!" squeaked Poppyseed, and ran as fast as he could up a tree. Luckily, the cat didn't follow him. From high up in the tree, Poppyseed could see the fairies getting ready for a lovely feast.

7. He suddenly realised that he hadn't stopped to eat anything for a whole day, and he was hungry. He crept right to the end of a branch, hoping to jump down on to the table without being seen. But at the moment when he jumped, the witch's spell wore off, and Poppyseed-the-mouse turned back to Poppyseed-the-elf.

8. The Fairy Queen was angry. "I see you are up to your tricks again," she said, "go to bed at once—without any supper." Poor Poppyseed! He sat sadly in bed while his tummy got emptier and emptier. But Rosepetal hadn't forgotten him. She brought him a tray of delicious things to eat. Don't you think that was kind of her?

One day when the sun was shining

One day when the sun was shining, naughty Grandpa Fox climbed out of bed and thought about rabbits.

That same morning, when that same big yellow sun was shining, good Goody Fox climbed out of his bed and he, too, thought about rabbits.

Naughty Grandpa Fox was thinking about setting a rabbit trap. He wanted to catch Mrs. Rabbit and her family of young rabbits,

to make a big juicy rabbit pie. Rabbit pie was Grandpa's favourite dish.

Goody Goody Fox was thinking that he would have to hurry to Mrs. Rabbit's house. He was going to collect Toddler Rabbit. Rabbits were Goody's favourite friends.

Mrs. Rabbit had a lot of young ones and young rabbits, just like young children, are always hungry. That meant Mrs. Rabbit had to go shopping every day.

Now, one of her youngsters called Toddler, liked to go shopping with his mummy. He was only a toddler though, and he was always picking up tins of things that rabbits couldn't eat and putting them in his mummy's basket. That meant Mrs. Rabbit had to walk round the shop again and put them all back.

So Goody and Mrs. Rabbit had arranged that when she was going shopping and there was no one in the burrow to look after Toddler, kind Goody Fox would look after him. Today was one of those days.

"Toddler's all ready," smiled Mrs. Rabbit when Goody arrived: "and here are some bricks for him to play with till I collect him."

Goody was happy. He was starting the day well by being a good Goody. "Come on Toddler," he said. "We'll hop, skip and jump all the way to my house."

* * *

"I'll nip over and see my grandson Goody, this morning," decided Grandpa Fox when he was ready to go out. "I'll try and teach him one or two things. Like how to catch rabbits and how to eat them. It's time he started to be more foxy!"

Grandpa raced round to Goody's house and he nearly fell over himself with joy when he saw Goody playing with Toddler.

"Aha! So Goody has my lunch," chuckled Grandpa Fox, "and he isn't the goody-goody he makes himself out to be, nor the goody-goody I thought he was turning into."

But Goody was a goody-goody—he couldn't help it—and when he saw Grandpa with a fork in his pocket, he was a worried goody-goody Goody.

Toddler was so busy playing that he didn't feel Grandpa's hot breath on his neck. Nor did he notice when Grandpa tapped his ear.

Goody knew that he had to protect

I am your grandpa and my name is Grandpa *Fox*. You must remember that I know foxy ways. In fact, I thought of some of them myself. *You* don't really believe all that silly nonsense about loving everyone and not eating rabbits. We *both* know it's not true. It isn't true, Goody, is it?'' asked Grandpa, beginning to wonder.

"Yes, it is!'' replied his grandson Goody, grandly, "and if you were just a little *less* mean and sly, and a little *more* kind and good, you would have a few friends around here, instead of a lot of enemies.''

Grandpa began to get cross.

Toddler right then and there. He snatched the little one up and put him behind his back.

"Ouch,'' cried Toddler.

He wondered what he could have done wrong to receive such rough treatment from his usually kind and good foxy friend. Then he heard Grandpa Fox's voice and he kept as still as a mouse when a cat's around.

"Now, now, Goody,'' grumbled Grandpa. "That's no way to treat my lunch—er, or is it my supper?''

Goody felt Toddler begin to shake behind him.

"Toddler is not your lunch, Grandpa and he's not going to be your supper either. I am being good, as usual. I'm helping Mrs. Rabbit by looking after Toddler while she does her shopping.''

"You can stop all that goody talk, Goody.

"What you don't seem to understand young fellow,'' he shouted, "is that I behave as a good fox should. Whoever heard of a fox being good. I've tried to teach you to be a good fox but it seems that you have turned out a very bad fox. In fact, you're so bad—because you're so good—that I begin

need any more lessons from me."

You can imagine how puzzled Goody was when, a few minutes later Grandpa seemed to be a charming old fox. With a crafty smile on his face he sat down on the grass beside young Toddler. Then he put an arm round Toddler.

Goody didn't like it.

Neither did Toddler. Not one bit. He looked round at Grandpa warily. Then he saw that Grandpa Fox had a brick in his hand and he brightened up very quickly. Grandpa Fox didn't want to hurt him. He just wanted to play bricks with him.

But Goody was still puzzled.

"I wonder what would make my sneaky Grandpa change so suddenly," asked Goody. "Whatever it is, it won't do rabbits any good. I know that."

Grandpa didn't let Goody stay puzzled

to wonder at times whether you are a real fox at all."

At the end of his speech Grandpa mopped his face.

It gave Goody a chance to turn round and make sure Toddler was still safe. "Don't worry, Toddler," he said. "I won't let Grandpa do anything to you."

Now, while Grandpa Fox was mopping his face, he moved his head, and his eyes opened very wide. For there, coming along the lane towards Goody's house, was Mrs. Rabbit and her son Jack.

"Ah, so that's it," thought Grandpa. "Dear Goody was just keeping the little rabbit happy in order to trap yet more of his delicious rabbit family so that we can have a bigger rabbit pie. What a good rabbit-catcher my grandson is. He doesn't

for long. He was too excited.

"I've seen them. I've seen them!" he chuckled behind his hand.

"Seen who?" queried Goody.

"Mrs. Rabbit and her son," Grandpa told him. "They are coming along the lane towards your house right now."

"Oh, no," said Goody.

But Grandpa wasn't listening. "I'll play with Toddler until they arrive," he went on, "then we can catch the three of them together. Oh, what a goody-goody foxy grandson you are."

Poor Goody!

He ran to the garden wall as fast as his legs would let him.

Grandpa was right. There they were.

Mrs. Rabbit and young Jack were on their way home from shopping already and they would soon be calling at Goody's house to collect Toddler.

"What a fix for a fox," Goody thought. "At least, it's a terrible fix for a goody fox like me. Grandpa seems to think that I've arranged for the rabbits to come here so that we can trap them and he can have a big rabbit pie. Well, he's not going to make rabbit pie from my friends. I won't have it. That's not being friendly."

Goody wanted to shout out to Mrs. Rabbit. He wanted to tell her and Jack to run away, but he couldn't. If he did, Grandpa was bound to hear him. Then what would happen to poor innocent little Toddler.

"Why, oh why, didn't Mrs. Rabbit spend more time walking round the shops today," cried Goody. "And why are they in such a hurry to get here. If only they would slow down a bit I could think of something to do."

Then Mrs. Rabbit saw Goody looking over the fence and pointed to him.

"Cooee," called Jack jumping about with pleasure when he saw Goody.

Goody quickly disappeared from view so that Jack wouldn't go on calling to him.

He walked up and down, and up and down his garden thinking.

Grandpa was still playing bricks with Toddler but he did notice Goody pacing

backwards and forwards across the garden.

He patted him on the back.

"Grandpa is proud of you, my boy," he said.

Goody didn't want to know.

He sat down on a stone to do some more thinking.

All the time, Mrs. Rabbit and her son Jack were getting nearer and nearer the cottage.

blackberry and apple pie, rabbit pie, gooseberry pie or chicken pie," Grandpa would say, "it must be cooked to a turn."

And he took his cookery book with him too, when he visited any of his friends, in case they offered him a nice tasty dish or two.

When it was cooking time, Grandpa would read the book and give out instructions, and whoever was cooking, had to follow the instructions very carefully. Then Grandpa would use his fork and poke things like carrots and potatoes and dumplings, to see if they were cooked enough.

Goody was used to it so he didn't mind too much but Grandpa's friends were often very angry.

Once everything was ready, Grandpa would then get down to using his fork for the right purpose. To eat his meal.

Well, Goody rushed straight across the garden, dived his hand into Grandpa's back trousers pocket and whipped out the book.

Suddenly Goody's eyes stopped looking sad and worried. They looked bright and cheerful instead. A happy smile spread across his face. He had thought of *something* at last.

Goody knew, of course, that whenever Grandpa carried his fork, Grandpa was hungry. Goody couldn't forget that because he often had to do the cooking, and when Grandpa was there, cooking wasn't an easy job.

The *something* Goody now remembered, was that Grandpa also carried a cookery book. He never ever went anywhere without it.

You see, Grandpa was very particular about the way things were cooked. Even when he was very very hungry, everything had to be cooked properly. "Cooked to a turn," was what he always told Goody.

"No matter what it is—pigeon pie,

"Come on, Grandpa. There's no time to waste," he said.

"I'm not wasting time," laughed Grandpa Fox, "if I'm keeping young Toddler happy. Believe you me."

Goody explained: "Grandpa, you are wasting time. You'll have to stop playing bricks with Toddler this minute. There's a lot of work to do. Just look at the heaps of things we need, to make a rabbit pie."

Goody lowered his voice: "You need more than rabbits, you know." He held the book open for Grandpa to see.

"Yes, yes. I know all about that," said Grandpa. "We need carrots and turnips and mushrooms and celery and potatoes and lots of other things."

"That's just the point," Goody told him. "You'll have to go and dig them up right away."

"D-d-d-dig them up," stuttered Grandpa.

"Yes. They're growing in my vegetable garden. *You* must hurry. Mrs. Rabbit and Jack are nearly here and if Mrs. Rabbit sees you, she will scamper away. So will Jack and, if he gets the chance, so will Toddler."

"Hmm. You may be right," muttered Grandpa, "but what are you going to do?"

"A goody-goody fox like me doesn't have to do anything. Mrs. Rabbit wouldn't think of running away from me. No one runs away from me. I'm everybody's friend."

Grandpa sniffed.

He was having second thoughts. He didn't like hard work, and digging up vegetables was very, very hard work.

"Oh well," he said at last. "You're most probably right. One look at me and those nice juicy-looking rabbits would be so frightened they would take all day to cook, and still be too tough to eat."

"They would," agreed Goody pushing his Grandpa in the direction of the vegetable garden. "Off you go."

And off went Grandpa.

"Whew," whistled Goody with relief as he watched Grandpa Fox trot away reading the cookery book.

He tiptoed towards Toddler.

"I'm pleased Grandpa Fox has gone away," said Toddler, "even if it is only to another part of the garden. I didn't like the way he kept looking at me. Now that he's gone, let's play with my bricks again".

Goody couldn't believe his ears.

"We're not playing bricks anymore today," Goody told him. "You don't know the danger you've been in. I suppose it's because you're a toddler."

And with that, Goody grabbed him by the hand and whisked him out of the garden.

Toddler flew through the air behind Goody.

"Where are we going?" he asked. I haven't picked up my bricks."

Goody wasn't worried about bricks. He wanted to reach the other side of his garden gate before Mrs. Rabbit and Jack.

He did.

Mrs. Rabbit was just arriving. "What's happened?" she asked. "What are you doing with Toddler?"

"Saving him," said an out-of-breath Goody. "And saving you, too. Don't stand about here looking bewildered. Grandpa thinks I've trapped you into coming here so that he can have rabbit pie."

"Oh no," whimpered Jack.

"Oh yes," said Goody. "He's digging up the vegetables now. Please go away."

Mrs. Rabbit didn't need another warning.

She grabbed hold of Toddler as well as Jack and they all fled along the lane.

Goody watched until his friends disappeared over the hill. "Oh, yes. I am being a good Goody Fox today," said he.

But what was he going to do now? There would be no rabbit pie for Grandpa's lunch or his supper and, although Goody had known there never was going to be a rabbit pie, Grandpa hadn't.

Foxy ideas come easily to foxes and Goody had one now.

He hurried back to his vegetable garden. "Grandpa! Grandpa! A dreadful disease has

attacked all the rabbits in these parts. Mrs. Rabbit wouldn't even come in, it's so dreadful. She says that bob-tail-moult has started and Doctor Rabbit has ordered all rabbits to bed for a week. Grandpa, what *is* bob-tail-moult?''

''Bob-tail-moult,'' explained Grandpa, ''is the same as our brush-moult when we lose the fur from our brush. But bob-tail-moult also means that foxes can't eat rabbits for two months, even though the rabbits only go to bed for a week. They just don't taste the same when their fur has been falling out of their bob-tail. Are you quite sure about this Goody?''

''Oh yes. I noticed Toddler's bob-tail was losing its fur,'' he said quickly.

You can tell Goody wasn't used to telling untruths, can't you? He quite forgot that he hadn't seen Toddler's bob-tail.

Happily for Goody, Grandpa forgot, too. He was so upset at not being able to eat rabbit pie for two months, he couldn't think of anything but being upset. Miserably he bounced a tomato up and down.

''I am sorry, Grandpa,'' said Goody, who wasn't really sorry at all. ''I'll get some lunch ready. Once you've had something to eat, you'll feel much better. You just stay there until I call. Lunch won't be long.''

Away raced Goody to Mrs. Rabbit.

''Please, Mrs. Rabbit, do you have a spare pie that I could give Grandpa for his lunch?'' asked breathless Goody.

''Here, take this. It's a vegetable pie,'' she told him. ''The biggest one I have. We're so happy to be out of your greedy Grandpa's

clutches that you are very welcome to it.''

The pie was still hot when Goody called. ''Lunch is ready, Grandpa.''

When Grandpa saw the pie his eyes lit up. ''I'm beginning to feel better already,'' he said. ''That pie is a very cheerful sight for an upset Grandpa on a bob-tail-moult day.''

Goody waited for Grandpa to taste it and when he saw the smile of pleasure on

Grandpa's face, he knew that Mrs. Rabbit had given him a delicious pie.

''I have taught you to be a good cook!'' laughed Grandpa, ''even if I haven't taught you to be a foxy fox.

But we know, don't we, that Goody Fox is a foxy fox. He certainly foxed Grandpa.

And Goody is keeping his fingers crossed that Grandpa doesn't find out!

Little Boy Blue

Little Boy Blue, come blow on your horn,
The sheep's in the meadow, the cow's in the corn.
Where is the boy who looks after the sheep?
He's under the haystack, fast asleep.
Will you wake him? No, not I,
For if I do, he's sure to cry.

1. Jamie and Jean lived in a village and went to the School on the Green. They were very excited one morning because they had a new teacher. "Good morning, children," she said.

2. All the children liked Miss Fair, and by break time she knew all their names. While they played outside, she went for coffee. She *was* surprised when a baby rabbit popped up in the milk jug.

3. She guessed that one of her children had put it there! She took it back to the classroom and gave them a lesson all about animals. "After lunch you must all bring a piece of fruit," said Miss Fair. "We will have a drawing lesson."

4. Jamie took a pear, and Jean a banana. There were apples, oranges, a bunch of grapes and a pineapple. "These will make a really nice picture," smiled Miss Fair.

"But before we start, we will ve a game of Ring-a-ring-a-ses," she went on.

6. It *was* fun. When the children came to the end of the song, they all fell down! Do you ever play that game?

7. But while they had been singing and dancing, the fat boy had eaten all the fruit except the pineapple.

8. So they drew pictures of him with the pineapple on his head, and then they learned the verse on the next page.

One Whistling Dancer

One whistling dancer,
Whistles while he whirls.

Two ballet dancers
Are very clever girls.

Three thirsty dancers
Drinking lemonade.

Four funny dancers
With bread and marmalade.

Five fairy dancers
Love the sunny weather.

Six Scottie dancers
Among the purple heather.

Seven Spanish dancers
Tango all the way.

Eight aching dancers
Danced too long all day.

Nine noisy dancers, Without a single friend.

Ten Toytown dancers, To make a happy end.

TEDDY IN TOYLAND

1. Do you like that toy clock Teddy has been playing with? He can twiddle the hands round and learn how to tell the time. After a lot of playing, Teddy fell into a nice deep sleep.

2. TOOT TOOTLE TOOOT TOOT TOOT! Suddenly a big blaring sound made Teddy almost jump out of his skin. Golly gosh! It was a trumpeter with a message from the queen at the royal palace.

3. "A message for you Mr. Bear," said the trumpeter. "Well, that's very nice I'm sure," replied Teddy crossly, "but did you have to make quite so much noise?" The trumpeter smiled.

4. "Everyone has to be wide awake to read a message from the queen," he explained. "Queens don't allow any mistakes, you know." The message said Teddy was to go to the palace.

5. Off Teddy went and there was the queen waiting to speak to him. "The toyland engineers have just made this nice new railway set," she said, "and I want you to play with it to see if it works."

6. "If you say the railway is nice, then we will make it for sending to children in the real world," explained the queen. Teddy was pleased. "The railway is lovely," he smiled. "It works properly."

HERE COMES
P.C. Bobby

1. P.C. Bobby was enjoying a pleasant stroll in Pixieland. Everyone was being very well-behaved that day, so the pixie policeman was having a nice little rest.

2. *Everyone* was being well-behaved did I say? H'mmm! I should have said everyone except Ernie the elephant. As P.C. Bobby walked by, Ernie blew off his hat!

5. Pixie Poppet showed P.C. Bobby where his yacht was floating out of reach, and Bobby knew just what to do about it. He went and fetched Ernie and led him to the pond.

6. Ernie was eager to make up for having been naughty earlier on. And here you can see how he rescued the yacht. He *blew* it across the pond!

3. "Now look here, Ernie," said P.C. Bobby crossly. "That was very naughty." And he was all set to give Ernie a scolding when along came young Pixie Poppet.

4. "Boo-hoo-hoo!" sobbed Pixie Poppet. "I was playing with my yacht at the park pond, but the breeze stopped blowing and my yacht's stuck in the pond."

7. "Well, done, Ernie," smiled P.C. Bobby. "That's much more useful than blowing people's hats off, you know."

8. Ernie just had to agree, because he liked being thanked *much* more than being scolded, and little Pixie Poppet thanked him *ever* so much for saving his toy yacht. Of course, Poppet thanked P.C. Bobby, too!

TOBY'S TEASERS

1 COMPLETE THIS PICTURE CROSSWORD BY WRITING IN THE NAMES OF THE OBJECTS ACROSS AND DOWN.

1. DOWN

1→ BUtterfly

2. DOWN

1. ACROSS

Bushes

3. ACROSS

2→ frag

2. ACROSS

3→ Wheel Barrow

2. CAN YOU HELP NANKU AND HIS FATHER FIND THEIR WAY TO THE IGLOO?

3. HERE ARE TWO LOVABLE LITTLE CREATURES CLIMBING UP A TREE. TO FIND OUT WHAT THEY ARE, JOIN UP THE DOTS, NUMBERS 1-48, WITH YOUR PENCIL.

ANSWERS. 1. BUTTERFLY, BRUSHES, FROG, FLAG, WHEELBARROW. 3. KOALA BEARS.

52

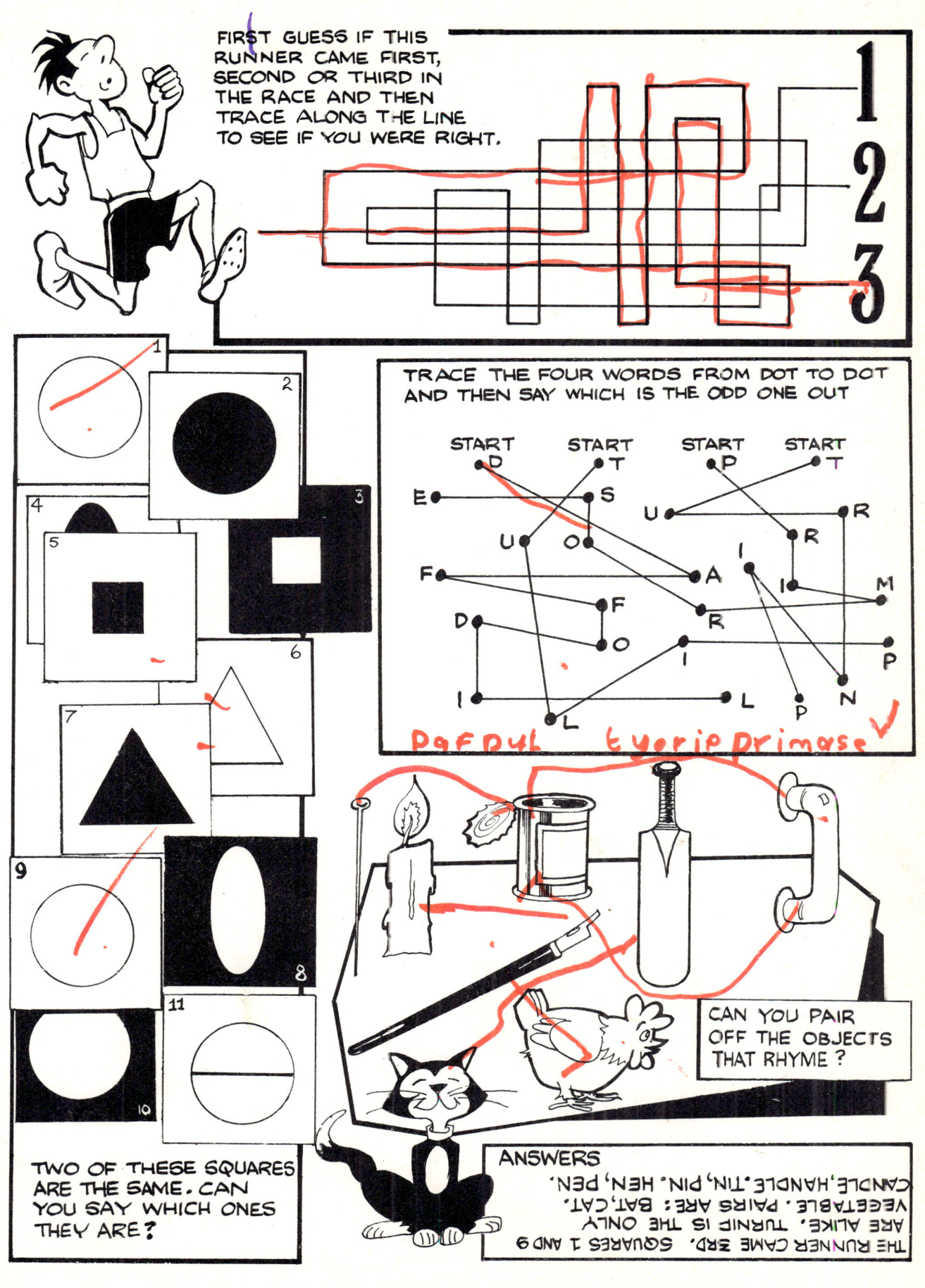

FIRST GUESS IF THIS RUNNER CAME FIRST, SECOND OR THIRD IN THE RACE AND THEN TRACE ALONG THE LINE TO SEE IF YOU WERE RIGHT.

TRACE THE FOUR WORDS FROM DOT TO DOT AND THEN SAY WHICH IS THE ODD ONE OUT

START
D

START
T

START
P

START
T

CAN YOU PAIR OFF THE OBJECTS THAT RHYME?

TWO OF THESE SQUARES ARE THE SAME. CAN YOU SAY WHICH ONES THEY ARE?

Fun at school with
Miss Muddle

MISS Muddle is the nice teacher of the first year infants' class at Jolly Towers School. You remember Miss Muddle, don't you? She is the lady who always seems to get into a muddle.

Sometimes, however, Miss Muddle has some really lovely ideas.

For instance, one morning, the boys and girls in Miss Muddle's class found that there was a bird table standing in the playground right outside one of the classroom windows.

Miss Muddle had made the bird table all by herself, with just a little help from Mr. Tidy, the school caretaker.

"Now, children," smiled Miss Muddle, "I have had this bird table set up so that you can watch the birds feeding. Let's see what happens when I put out some food for them, shall we?"

Miss Muddle opened the window, leaned out and scattered a handful of seeds on the bird table.

"These seeds are special wild bird food," Miss Muddle explained to her class as they gathered round to watch. "They should attract all kinds of pretty birds to the window ledge, and while they are feeding you will be able to draw them and colour your drawings."

Don't you think that was a splendid idea? The boys and girls in Miss Muddle's class certainly thought so, because just as they were getting out their reading books, two sparrows came fluttering down to feed off the bird table!

So instead of doing lessons, the children were allowed to take out their pencils to draw the birdies.

Soon after, the sparrows were joined by a blackbird and a bluetit. That meant the children were allowed to go on

drawing for a little longer until all the birds had flown off.

"On with our reading lesson now, children," said Miss Muddle. "The birds must be fed only once a day, or we'll never get any work done — and the birds would grow so fat that they wouldn't be able to fly!"

How the class laughed at that. Miss Muddle does say some funny things to her pupils, doesn't she?

Anyway, next morning, Miss Muddle was just giving out sheets of drawing paper to the children when she realised there were no birds at the bird table.

"Dear me! I wonder why that is . . ." muttered Miss Muddle.

"Please, Miss, I think it's because you haven't put out any food today," suggested Terry helpfully.

"Goodness!" gasped Miss Muddle. "I seem to have muddled things again! I thought I told one of *you* to do it, but I suppose I must have forgotten. . . . Well, I will put out the food today, but as from tomorrow, children, it will be *your* job to see that the birds are fed. The seed packet

"Oh, dear," she sighed. "I cannot let you put out so much food every day, children. I suppose I shall have to do the job myself, though it seems a pity. And I am *sure* to forget! Golly, what a fine muddle this has turned out to be."

Don't worry though, girls and boys. Everything was soon to work out very well — thanks to an idea Belinda had.

"Please, Miss Muddle," she began, "couldn't we each have a special day for bird-feeding? You could write our names against the dates on the calendar, then there wouldn't be any quarrelling! And I could be one of the first to have a turn because the first letter in my name is near the beginning of the alphabet!"

Miss Muddle thought that was a jolly good idea.

"My, my! Whatever would I do without you children to get me out of my muddles?" she said with a smile.

The boys and girls *did* feel pleased with themselves. That's why they like to help Miss Muddle, you know — because she makes them feel so grown-up.

will be kept beside the window.'

At the time, Miss Muddle did not realise the muddle that her idea was going to cause. However, she very soon found out — the very next morning, in fact!

You see, when Miss Muddle walked into the classroom, all the boys and girls were crowded round the window, looking a little anxious. And outside the window there seemed to be about a *hundred* birds clustered round the bird table, all pecking and squawking and squabbling!

Miss Muddle dashed across to open the window, and the birds flew away.

"Dear, oh dear!" puffed Miss Muddle. "There is far too much bird seed on the table. Which one of you put out the food for the birds today?"

At once, there were cries of: "Me, Miss Muddle!" or "Please, Miss Muddle, it was me," or "No you didn't — *I* did!"

In fact, *every* child in the class had put out some food for the birds, because no-one wanted to be left out of things.

Poor Miss Muddle hadn't *dreamt* that would happen.

Patty and her Magic Puppy

1. Well now, this is the story I mentioned at the end of the ''Patty and her Magic Puppy'' story on Pages 12 and 13, and it begins with Patty and her mummy and Poppy going for a nice long walk.

2. The trouble was (just as in that other story) it began to rain. Now Mummy was wearing a lovely new coat that day, and she was a little upset at the thought of getting it wet. Still, she needn't have worried.

3. Poppy the puppy quickly came to Mummy's aid. The puppy trotted over to a toadstool and wagged that wonderful magic tail of hers. And just *look* at what happened !

4. The toadstool grew and *grew* and *GREW* until it was just like a large umbrella. So Mummy's coat was still quite dry when they got back home ! Hurray ! Well done, Poppy !

Patty's Puppy Puzzle

Patty has a special little puzzle for you, girls and boys. In the picture above are six of Poppy's puppy playmates, and what you have to do is name the breed of each puppy.

It will help you a little to know that each puppy's name begins with the same letter as the name of its breed, and their names are Pompom, Perry, Lex, Corky, Shep and Amber.

ANSWERS:
Pompom is a Poodle; Perry is a Peke; Lex is a Labrador; Corky is a Cocker Spaniel; Shep is a Shetland Sheepdog and Amber is an Alsatian.

 # Mary
and her dolls

1. Mary was always very busy looking after her toys. One afternoon, she decided that her woolly dog, Fluff, needed a bath. "You come and watch," she said to her doll, who was called Fenella.

2. Fenella wasn't very pleased about that. "I want to have a ride in our pedal car," she complained. "You must wait until I have finished drying Fluff," said Mary. "I won't be very long. I've nearly finished."

3. Suddenly there was a ring at the doorbell. Mary put down Fluff and went to open the front door. Standing outside was Teddy from next door. "I've come to play with Fluff and Fenella," he said.

4. "Come in, Teddy," smiled Mary. "Oh, what a lovely car," said Teddy. "May I ride in it?" "No, you can't," said Fenella, "it's my turn." "It isn't," shouted Fluff, "it's *my* turn to have a ride first."

5. Mary was cross. "You must learn to share things," she told them. "Of course Teddy may have a ride. And because you have been so rude and selfish Fenella and Fluff, I will not give you any tea."

6. So Teddy had a lovely ride in the car, and when it was time for tea Mary gave him lemonade and biscuits. Fenella didn't have any. Nor did Fluff. They did feel sorry for themselves, not having any tea.

7. After tea, Teddy had to go home. Mary put on his hat and coat and opened the door for him. "Goodbye," she called, "come and play with us again soon!" Fenella and Fluff watched him go.

8. Mary looked at her two toys and laughed. "You *do* look miserable," she said. "Cheer up! You can have your ride now, Fenella. And Fluff, here are some biscuits!" So everyone was happy.

Mary's Riddles

What bird can lift heavy weights?   A crane.

What has a mouth, but no eyes or nose?   A river.

Grandma— next door

ONE day during the school holidays, Pam and Paul were about to set off for the cinema with Mummy, when who should they meet at the front gate but Grandma.

Mind you, that didn't surprise the children too much. You see, Grandma lives just next door, and every day at the same time she goes off to work at the corner shop where she has a part-time job.

"Hello, Grandma," beamed Paul. "We are going to the *pictures* today !"

"My, aren't you lucky ?" smiled Grandma. "I wish I could go with you, but work comes first, I'm afraid. Ah, well. I hope you enjoy the film, my loves !"

Of course, Pam and Paul *did* enjoy the film very much. It was all about pirates and treasure and exciting things like that. So later, when it was over and Mummy was making the tea, Pam and Paul rushed next door to tell Grandma about their treat.

Grandma was thrilled.

"I wish I could go to the cinema more often these days," she said with rather a wistful look on her face. "But I can't really afford to."

Then she added more brightly : "I used to go to the pictures *lots,* you know ! I saw all those wonderful old Hollywood films you see on television nowadays. I always thought that the musicals were the best. I do love musicals !"

Well, Pam and Paul were thoughtful as they ate their tea that evening. They wondered how they could help Grandma to go to the pictures more often.

After tea, the answer came to Pam and Paul in a flash ! It happened like this.

Mummy had bought a filmgoer's magazine at the cinema, and she and Daddy were busy trying to complete a crossword puzzle inside the magazine. The puzzle was all about old films and film stars.

"It's a competition," explained Mummy. "The first ten correct entries will win a free seat at the cinema for a whole year ! Wouldn't that be lovely ?"

"H'mm, it would indeed," chuckled Daddy, "but we haven't much hope of winning ! We are both too young to answer all these questions about old films."

Pam looked at Paul and Paul looked at Pam, and they both began to grin broadly.

They knew someone who was old enough to know the answers to those questions. Do you know who it was ? Yes, it was *Grandma!*

Well, the very next morning, first thing, Pam and Paul took the film magazine round to Grandma's house.

"There's a crossword puzzle in here that Mummy was trying to do last night," said Paul, waving the magazine about.

"Yes, and we thought we'd surprise her by finishing it," went on Pam, "with a little help from *you* of course, Grandma !"

"Why, I'd be pleased to help," chuckled Grandma. "Read out the clues, Paul."

So Pam and Paul sat down at the table, and Paul read the clues aloud. And do you know, Grandma was able to answer them all without any trouble ! She just sat there nodding and smiling, and saying things like : "Oh, that's easy ! It was Laurel and Hardy," or "Ah, yes. Calamity Jane — I remember that film well !"

Pam filled in all the answers in ink, in her best hand-writing. Mind you, sometimes she had to ask Grandma how to spell some of the names, but between them they completed the crossword in the end.

"Thank you so much, Grandma," giggled Pam at last. "You have been a great help." And off she went with Paul, the pair of them grinning from ear to ear.

You see, the children were keeping a big secret from Grandma. I wonder if you can guess what it was.

Anyway, two weeks later, Grandma found out. She came hurrying round to Mummy's kitchen one morning, waving a piece of paper in the air. In fact, Grandma was so excited that she could hardly speak !

"This . . . this is a voucher, dear," she explained to Mummy at last. "It lets me have a free seat at the cinema for a year ! But . . . but I don't understand why it's been sent to *me !* There must be some mistake. . . ."

"There's no mistake, Grandma," piped up Paul. "You gave us the answers to that film crossword puzzle, remember ?"

"It was a *competition,* Grandma," explained Pam. "We wrote your name and address on the entry form and posted it off right away. We wanted you to win so you could go to the pictures every week. Well, now you can !"

For a moment, Mummy and Grandma couldn't believe it.

"Gosh, you clever things !" chuckled Mummy to the children.

"Clever ?" gasped Grandma. "Why, they are a pair of absolute *dears !*"

And as Grandma gave them a hug, Pam and Paul were the proudest grandchildren in the whole wide world !

SCRIBBLETIME

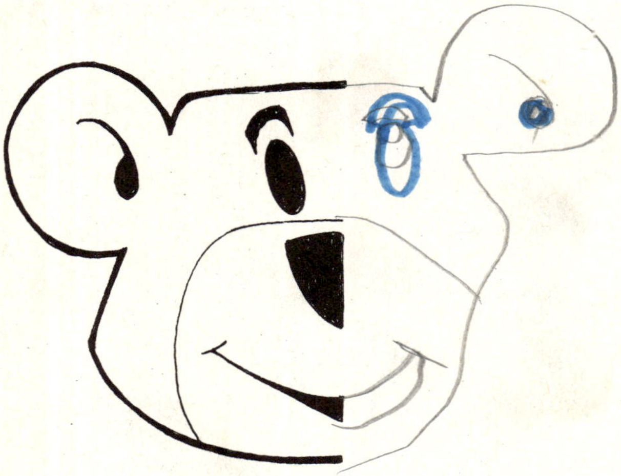

Draw a line from dot number 1 to dot number 2. And so on until you reach dot number 43.

HOW GOOD AN ARTIST ARE YOU? SEE IF YOU CAN COMPLETE THE OTHER SIDE OF THESE FUNNY ANIMALS' FACES.

IF YOU CANNOT GUESS WHAT IS IN THIS PICTURE, ALL YOU HAVE TO DO IS SHADE ALL THE AREAS MARKED WITH A DOT WITH A PENCIL.

SEE IF YOU CAN FIT THE NAMES OF THESE THINGS INTO THE SQUARES BELOW.

3 ACROSS

2 DOWN

1 ACROSS

1 DOWN

COPY THE HEAD OF THIS GIRAFFE. OUR ARTIST HAS PUT IN SOME LINES TO GUIDE YOU. THE SQUARES WILL MAKE IT QUITE EASY TO DO.

Two little Scamps and Mustard

1. The Scamps' mother gave them a lovely new toy one day. It was a jolly Jack-in-the-box, and the Scamps played with it so much that Mustard, the rabbit, began to feel lonely.

2. Anyway, the two Scamps had *another* nice surprise that day. Later on, they found a big cardboard box that they hadn't seen before. Ooh! I wonder what was inside it.

3. "Let's take a peep!" said the two little Scamps. They lifted the lid, and out sprang a *Mustard*-in-the-box! Wasn't that a funny trick Mustard had played on the Scamps?

4. "Oh, dear!" smiled the Scamps. "Did we forget about you because of our new toy? Still, you *know* we love *you* best of all!" And that made Mustard feel very happy.

Lots of little girls and boys
Like teddies, dolls and other toys,
But Jill says "Nothing can compare
With my little Panda Bear."

65

TOBY and the lost Purse

A lovely tale about your favourite friend

1. One day Toby Terrier's mummy dashed out shopping very early, so Daddy and Toby had to wash up the breakfast things.

2. "Well, I'm glad I don't have to do that every day," smiled Daddy. Then Mummy came home with a bagful of shopping.

3. "Cheerio then, I'm off to work," smiled Daddy. Toby was watching what Mummy was taking from the shopping basket.

4. At last, at the very bottom, was what Toby had been waiting for. His favourite biscuits ! But just look at the basket !

5. The weight of the shopping had split a hole in the bottom of the basket. "My purse must have fallen through, gasped Mummy.

6. "I'm sure my purse *was* in the basket," wailed Mummy. "It must have fallen out along the lane." Toby ran out to find it.

7. "Poor Mummy!" thought Toby. "She is so upset at losing her purse. I must find it for her." On and on he trotted.

8. Toby had scurried half way into town when he saw Romany Bear asleep by his caravan—and Toby saw something else.

9. Toby saw his mummy's purse on the step of the caravan. "I will just take the purse without disturbing Romany," thought Toby.

10. You see, Romany did look rather big and fierce and Toby was just a little bit afraid of him. Unluckily Romany woke up. Golly!

11. Romany didn't look a bit friendly, so Toby raced off with the purse, as fast as he could go. "Come back!" called Romany.

12. "Romany must have found Mummy's purse and planned to keep it for himself," puffed Toby, climbing a tree to hide.

13. "Well, I won't let him get it again," panted Toby, feeling clever as Romany Bear ran past the tree without seeing him.

14. When he thought that Romany had gone, Toby slithered down the tree. "Now to go home," he smiled. "I've outwitted Romany."

15. But Toby was feeling pleased too soon. As he trotted up a hump-backed bridge from *one* side, Romany strode up the *other*.

16. "Give me back that purse, you rascal," shouted Romany. Toby skipped on to the wall and dodged out of Romany's reach.

18. "EEEEEK!" shrieked Romany Bear, as he lost his balance. Then — SPLOSH! He made a huge splash, as he landed in the river.

17. "You won't escape," gasped Romany, grabbing at Toby. But Toby was young and frisky and he dodged out of the way.

19. Then Mummy ran up holding a purse just like the one Toby was holding. "I've found my purse in my pocket," she called.

20. Golly! It turned out that the purse Toby had taken was Romany's. But it looked just like Mummy's. Oh dear! Oh dear!

21. Toby was terribly sorry and to make up for all the trouble, Mummy gave Romany some dry clothes and a lovely dinner.

Jonathan Muddles

Do you ever have trouble saying difficult words? Lots of little children do, and it isn't until they are much older that they learn how to say some hard words properly.

This is a story about a little boy who was always getting words muddled up. For a start, he had trouble with his own name, which was Jonathan. He tried very hard to say Jonathan, but always ended up with "Jothing", or "Jonnen."

In the end, his mummy solved the problem by calling him Jon, and Jonathan could say *that* all right.

Jon's baby sister was called Elizabeth, and poor Jon couldn't manage that at all. To him, she was "Sillybet". It was no use mummy complaining that it was a most peculiar name, and please would Jon call his sister "Liz" or something easy like that. "Sillybet" she stayed.

"You *do* get muddled, Jon," said mummy. "I think I will call you Jonathan Muddles."

One morning Jon came down to breakfast, cheerful as ever. He sat down, and mummy said: "What would you like on your bread-and-butter?"

"Marbilly, please," said Jon, and his mother smiled and passed him the marmalade. At least she could tell that he didn't mean honey!

Jon's father was a farmer. So after breakfast he ran down to the barn to see if daddy was there. But the big barn was empty.

Then Jon looked round the back of the barn, but he still couldn't see his daddy. Instead, he saw a pretty bird sitting on a branch of a birch tree and a duck swimming happily round the farmyard pond.

"Are you enjoying your dapple, Mister Duck?" he called

Now the duck knew Jon and it realised Jon was trying to say "paddle", not dapple. It didn't argue,

either. It just said: "I'm having a lovely swim. Are you looking for your daddy? I saw him going down to the big field with the tractor."

Jon was disappointed, but not for long. "Mummy says I am not lallowed to go down to the big field," he said. "But never mind, I will stay here and talk to you insed."

He sat down by the side of the barn.

"Do you like my hat?" he asked the duck. "I love the feller in my hat, don't you? It's not a duck's feller," he added quickly, for he didn't want to hurt the duck's feelings.

The duck laughed out loud. "It's a very smart feather," it quacked. "Try saying it slowly. Fea-ther, fea-ther."

"That's what I *did* say," said Jon happily. "Fe-ller, fe-ller!"

"It's no good," said the bird to the duck. "I've tried myself. His daddy says he'll grow out of it in the end."

So after that, they both took no notice of Jonathan's muddles.

Jon stayed all morning chatting to his friends, while the duck swam round and round, and the bird hopped about.

Then, when his tummy told him it was time for lunch, he got up to go.

"Boodye," he said to the duck and the bird. "I must go now, 'cos Mummy said she was making my faithery lunch."

"What does faithery mean?" the duck whispered to the bird. "Favourite!" whispered the bird back.

"And what *is* your favourite lunch?" called the duck as Jon started home.

"BESKETTI," shouted Jon, and disappeared.

Can you tell what he meant? I expect you've guessed. He meant spaghetti, didn't he?

Baa, Baa, Black Sheep

OLD Granny Weller the story teller invited her favourite children to tea one day, and just as they were settling down to eat, one little boy began to hum the tune of that well-known nursery rhyme, "Baa, Baa, Black Sheep".

"Ah, that reminds me of an old story about a black sheep!" smiled Granny Weller. "Would you like to hear it?"

Well, if you would like to know the story about the black sheep, here it is, just as Granny Weller told it that day:

Once upon a time, there lived a little boy called Tom.

Now Tom was a good and happy child, but he was often lonely, too, for he had no brothers or sisters.

Tom's parents wished they could buy a pet to keep him company, but they could not afford such things.

So Tom had to go on being lonely — until one day, he saw a shepherd driving a big black sheep before him.

"Mother! Father!" cried Tom. "Come and see this sheep. It's as black as coal! I've never seen such a black sheep."

The shepherd let Tom give his black sheep a tit-bit.

"Pretty little Blacklocks," sighed Tom to the sheep. "I am sure you would be a wonderful pet for me...."

"Well, since the sheep is no use to me, I will give her to you good folks for only a shilling!" offered the shepherd. "You see, she isn't really mine. She is a stray which I found amongst my flock. I took her to market, but nobody wanted to buy her; because black wool is hard to dye, I suppose. Besides, she has a mean look about her!"

"I don't care," said Tom. "I am sure she is very nice underneath that curly coat."

Well, Tom's father and mother could see that the young boy's heart was set on keeping the black sheep, so they bought her from the shepherd for a shilling.

From that day on, Tom and Blacklocks (as Tom had named her) played everywhere together. Tom looked after the sheep and told her all his secrets.

Then one day, when they had been playing together down by the stream, Tom decided he was too tired to walk home. So he climbed on to Blacklocks' back and told her to carry him home.

"Dear Blacklocks," smiled Tom. "You are a wonderful, gentle pet. You are so good and kind...."

All at once there was a strange, bright flash, and Tom felt himself being thrown to the ground!

Shaken but unhurt, Tom picked himself up. However, he almost fell down again in astonishment when he saw what had happened to Blacklocks. She was no longer a sheep but a *princess,* with long, raven-black hair and a flowing black velvet cloak!

"Tom, you have broken the spell on me!" she said, smiling. "I am Princess Petunia, and once upon a time I was horrid and mean to everyone. Once, in a fit of temper, I was unkind to a little dog — but that little dog turned out to be a fairy in disguise! She changed me into a black sheep to teach me a lesson, and she said I would live on as a sheep until someone told me I was good and kind!"

"But — but you *are* good and kind!" blurted out Tom, still very bewildered.

"Yes, now I am — thanks to you, Tom," went on the Princess. "You have made me realise how nasty and selfish I was before. But never again will I be horrid or mean."

Princess Petunia was true to her word. She asked Tom and his parents to come and live in her palace, and she gave Tom fine clothes and a lovely *pony* for a pet!

In fact, Princess Petunia changed so much for the better that very soon everyone grew to love her — especially dear little Tom, of course!

73

Bella and the Prince

1. One day two beautiful princesses walked past the cottage of a poor old man. They were twins. Bella was kind and friendly – her sister Beatrice was cold and haughty.

2. Bella stopped to talk to the old man. "What can I do for you?" she asked as she stepped inside his cottage. Suddenly, lightning flashed, and a young prince stood there.

3. Bella cried out in alarm, and the prince said: "Do not be afraid, beautiful princess. A wicked witch put a curse on me, and the only way I can break the spell is to fall in love with a princess. I will only stay a prince as long as you are by my side – the moment you leave, I will change back into an old man." Bella liked the prince very much.

4. From then on, Bella often went to see the old man, and as long as she was by his side he changed back into a prince. But Beatrice was curious and jealous. "I must find out why Bella visits that old man," she thought. One day, she locked Bella in her room and crept out of the castle.

5. Beatrice flung open the door of the cottage and stamped inside. The old man was sitting alone, and he explained about the witch's curse. "Bella and I will be married soon," he said.

6. "I don't believe it," said Beatrice crossly. "*You* are no prince! *I* could fall in love with you, if you were." The old man shook his head. "You love only yourself," he told her sadly.

7. For the first time in her life, someone had told Beatrice the truth about herself. She was very thoughtful as she walked home to the castle. And from then on, whenever the prince came to visit Bella to make wedding plans, she tried hard not to be jealous or selfish or haughty. She tried to be as nice as her sister Bella.

8. At last the wedding day came, and Bella married her handsome prince who would never more turn back into a poor old man. Beatrice was their bridesmaid, and she was so pleased to see how happy the bride and bridegroom were that the beautiful twin sisters finally seemed to be true twins — alike in *every* way.

TEDDY IN TOYLAND

1. "Puff! Pant! Grunt! Gasp!" Teddy Bear was working very hard out in the meadow where his horse, Dobbin, lived. Teddy was building a cosy stable ready for the winter.

2. You see, although Dobbin was cheeky, Teddy still loved him and he didn't want Dobbin to be cold when the winter winds blew and the snow swirled round the bushes. Teddy went on working.

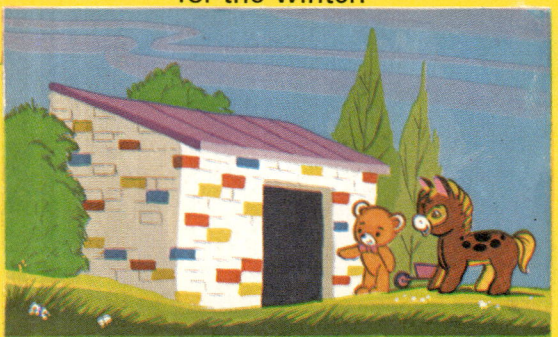

3. He built the stable out of his toy bricks, which snapped together, like the toy bricks you use I'm sure. "Here you are then, Dobbin," smiled Teddy, when the stable was finished.

4. "I will put some hay and straw inside and then you will be cosy," smiled Teddy. Dobbin was so pleased that he gave Teddy a big, wet kiss. Moo-moo the cow was watching.

5. "Perhaps if I give Teddy Bear a nice big, wet, lickey kiss, he will build me a cosy stable too," thought Moo-moo. She sidled up to Teddy, blinked shyly and gave him the kiss. He was surprised. He nearly fell over backwards.

6. Now, big, wet, lickey kisses are not that nice and when not only Moo-moo, but also Cow-cow tried to kiss Teddy, he decided to run away with Moo-moo and Cow-cow following him. "The farmer must build *your* stable," he called.

SANTA CLAUS

If you dream of Santa Claus,
Whoever you may be,
He will leave you presents,
On your Christmas tree.

Santa Claus is coming;
Christmas again is here;
Santa Claus is coming
Through the sky so clear.

John Metters